Why should I walk more often?

one small step

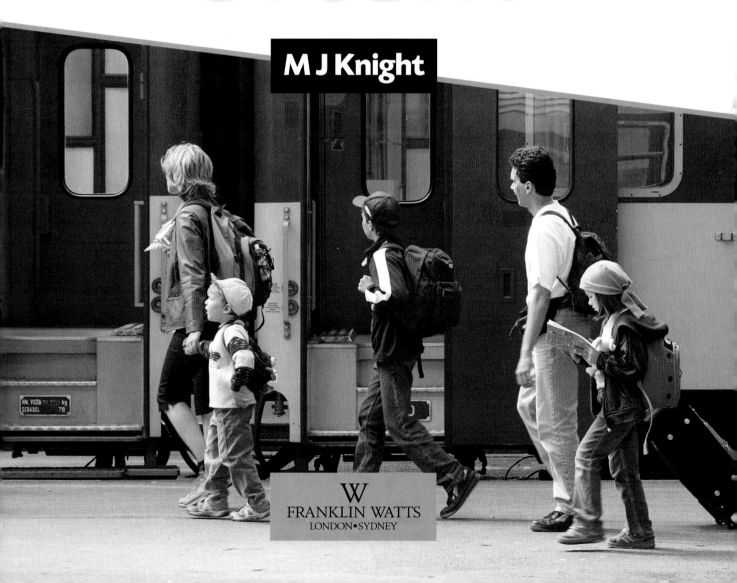

M J Knight

FRANKLIN WATTS
LONDON•SYDNEY

An Appleseed Editions book

First published in 2008 by Franklin Watts
338 Euston Road, London NW1 3BH

Franklin Watts Australia
Hachette Children's Books
Level 17/207 Kent St, Sydney, NSW 2000

© 2008 Appleseed Editions

Created by Appleseed Editions Ltd,
Well House, Friars Hill, Guestling,
East Sussex TN35 4ET

Designed by Guy Callaby
Edited by Jinny Johnson
Illustrations by Hel James
Picture research by Su Alexander

ISBN: 978 0 7496 8049 7

Dewey Classification: 363.73

A CIP catalogue for this book is available from the British Library.

Picture acknowledgements
Title page: Stewart Iskow/Alamy; 4 Claro Cortes IV/Reuters/Corbis;
5 Katsutoshi Hatsuzawa/NEOVISION/Getty Images; 7 Frederic Neema/
Sygma/Corbis; 8 Davis Gray/Reuters/Corbis; 9 Paul Souders/Corbis;
11 ilian car/Alamy; 12 By Ian Miles-Flashpoint Pictures/Alamy; 14 Tom
Stewart/Corbis; 15 Trevor Hyde/Alamy; 16 Stewart Iskow/Alamy;
18 Rainman/Zefa/Corbis; 19 Weberfoto/Alamy; 20 Julia Waterlow; Eye
Ubiquitous/Corbis; 21 Paulo Fridman/Corbis; 22 Reuters/Corbis;
23 Hans Reinhard/Zefa/Corbis; 25 Arctic-Images/Corbis; 27 David
Hancock/Handout/epa/Corbis; 28 William Campbell/Still Pictures;
29 Gerolf Kalt/Zefa/Corbis. Front cover: Fotosonline/Alamy.

Printed in China

Franklin Watts is a division of Hachette Children's Books

Contents

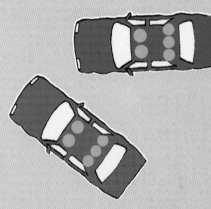

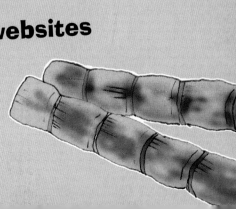

Leave the car at home

Walking is fun, free and helps you stay fit. There are lots of reasons to walk more often.

But many people drive short distances when they could walk, cycle or catch a bus or a train. All vehicles give off fumes as they are driven around. The fumes pollute the air, making it dirty.

The cars in this traffic jam in China are giving off lots of fumes which make the air unhealthy to breathe.

In towns and cities, where there are lots of vehicles, you can smell the fumes. The vehicles make so many fumes that they are changing the gases in the air around the Earth. And that's changing the weather.

Good for you too

Walking or riding a bike instead of taking the car means fewer fumes and the exercise is good for your body too. People inside a car on a busy road breathe in more dirty fumes than people walking along the pavement.

Walking to school every day is good for you and fun.

A step in the right direction

You might think that what you do doesn't matter, but it does. It matters very much. Every time you decide to walk, scoot, cycle or take a bus or train instead of going somewhere in a car you take a step in the right direction. You can make a difference – everyone can. If lots of people take a step in the right direction, even a small one, these small steps will add up to one big step.

What happens to traffic fumes?

Every time someone starts an engine, fumes come out of the exhaust pipe at the back of the vehicle.

An engine makes a gas called carbon dioxide, which blows out of the exhaust pipe. The carbon dioxide gas from exhausts mixes with all the gases in the air we breathe. These are part of a thick layer of gases around the Earth called the atmosphere.

The atmosphere lets through the sun's rays, which keep the Earth nice and warm – but not too hot. The rays bounce off the Earth and back into space.

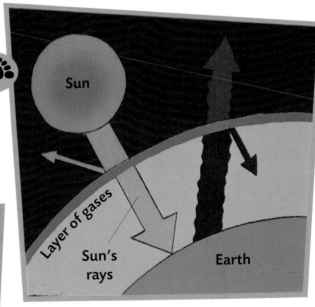

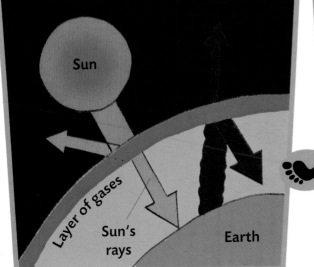

But when all the gases from car exhausts and other fumes mix with the atmosphere they help to keep more of the sun's heat near the Earth. This means the Earth is very slowly getting warmer.

To stop the Earth getting warmer everyone needs to try to make less carbon dioxide. One way we can do this is to drive less often.

I can make a difference

Does your family own a car? If so, do you use it a lot? Can you think of ways your family could use the car less? How about walking to local shops or markets instead of driving to a big supermarket. Or you could have your shopping delivered. That way, just one van drives to lots of different houses, and families need to make fewer car journeys. Look at supermarket websites to find out more.

How fumes change the weather

Have you noticed that our weather seems to be changing? This is partly because of all the fumes given off from car exhausts.

Lots of places are having more storms and rain. Other parts of the world desperately need more rain. The weather on Earth has always changed, but it seems to be changing faster than ever before. Scientists call this climate change.

Cracks in dry ground in southern Australia in 2007, during the worst drought for 100 years.

One small fact
Scientists in California have found that fumes from car exhausts might be making it rain less than it used to in dry areas.

Climate change means that the Earth is slowly getting warmer. Some of the water which is frozen at the North and South Poles is starting to melt and run into the seas. In time the melting ice will make the water level in the seas rise. This could cause problems for people who live on low islands or near coasts which are not very high above the sea.

The warmer temperatures on Earth seem to be causing more extreme weather too. More areas are being flooded than ever before, and more people don't have enough water to live.

Water streams off the edges of a melting iceberg in Greenland.

I can make a difference

Friends of the Earth

WWF

See what you can find out about climate change in the library or on a computer. You could look at the websites of groups which try to slow down climate change, such as Friends of the Earth, the World Wildlife Fund or Greenpeace.

GREENPEACE

Travelling to school

Lots of children go to school in a car every day. Are you one of them?

Ask your teacher if you can do a survey of all the children in your class, or even in your school, and find out how many travel to school by car. Get together with some friends and make a form like this, then fill it in every day.

HOW DID YOU TRAVEL TO AND FROM SCHOOL TODAY?		Alan	Amanda	Andy	Craig	Denise	Ellen	Freddie	Harry	Isobel	Mel
Walked/ scooted	To school	✓	✓		✓			✓	✓		
Walked/ scooted	From school	✓	✓		✓			✓	✓		
Cycled	To school				✓						
Cycled	From school										✓
By bus/ By train	To school							✓			✓
By bus/ By train	From school							✓	✓		
By car	To school	✓							✓		
By car	From school	✓									

After a week, have a look at all the information you have collected and work out how many children come to school in a car. You could follow up by finding out how far people have to travel to school. Then talk about ways to help children make fewer journeys by car. Turn the page for some ideas about this.

School journeys

● In the UK only about half of all children walk or cycle to school.

● The number of children who go to school in a car has doubled in the last 20 years.

● During the morning rush hour, 20 per cent of cars on the roads are taking children to school.

Yellow school buses take more than 25 million American schoolchildren to school and home again every day.

11

Take the walking bus

There are lots of ways to get to school without being a passenger in a car making a special journey.

Today children in many countries go to school every morning by walking bus. Mums and dads can help with this. A walking bus is lots of children walking together with a few parents who make sure everyone gets to school safely. The bus starts off from the home furthest away from school and stops at places on the way so children can join the group.

Walking to school with a walking bus is a great way to keep fit and catch up with all the news.

I can make a difference

Could you design a poster to ask everyone who comes by car to try coming a different way? Lots of schools around the world have a Walk to School week. Ask if you can have one in your school (see websites, page 31). You could have a prize for children who walk most often, or children who walk the furthest. Even people who always come by car might try travelling a different way once a week.

NEXT WEEK IS

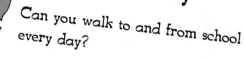

WALK TO SCHOOL WEEK

12 – 17 May

Can you walk to and from school every day?

Personal passports for everyone – get your stamp at the school gate

Prizes for everyone who walks all week!

Ask your parents to leave the car at home!

Why it's good to walk

Walking to school helps you get to know your neighbourhood better. People who walk can take short cuts through parks, green spaces and alleyways where cars can't go. It's also great exercise and wakes you up in the morning. Walking one and a half kilometres in 20 minutes uses as much energy as:

● running the same distance in ten minutes;
● swimming breaststroke for ten minutes;
● playing football for 12 minutes.

On your bike!

Do you own a bike? How often do you use it?

Have you thought about cycling to school or going on your bike to visit friends? Today, lots of cities have special cycle routes, which help to keep cyclists away from cars and other traffic.

When you cycle you can beat traffic jams, and it keeps you healthy too. Some schools run cycle training. If your school doesn't, look at the websites about cycle training on page 31 for information. You might even be able to persuade some parents to run an after-school bike club.

Wearing a helmet when you ride a bike protects your head.

One small fact
One out of every three children would prefer to cycle to school if they had a choice.

Bikes for hire

Some cities, such as Paris in France and Copenhagen in Denmark, have started a scheme for hiring bikes. Thousands of bikes are left in bike stands for people to hire by unlocking them with a special card. The bikes can be taken back in lots of different places, so you don't need to make a return journey to put them back. In Paris, the bikes were hired more than a million times in the first three weeks!

Why it's good to cycle

● Cycling is the least polluting way of travelling after walking.

● In the UK three-quarters of people live within three kilometres of a cycle route.

● Ten bikes can be parked in the space of one car.

x10

x1

Taking the bus or the train

How often do you travel by bus, train or tram?

If there isn't a railway station near you, there's probably a bus stop not far away. Travelling by bus or train pumps fewer fumes into the atmosphere – and it's more fun than driving in a car. You meet more people, no one has to worry about driving or losing the way, and it often doesn't cost a lot. You can get to know your local area better by bus or tram and take the train for special days out.

Some cities around the world allow children to travel free on buses, and most rail companies have family railcards so children can travel cheaply with their families.

This family is taking a trip by train from Prague in the Czech Republic.

Car Free Day

People in cities in more than 30 countries take part in a Car Free Day every year in September. Hundreds of cities, from Paris in France to Bangkok in Thailand, take part every year. The aim is for as many people as possible to leave the car at home and travel a different way. Car Free Day is part of Mobility Week, which has been held every year since 2002.

I can make a difference

Could your family use the bus or train when you go out for the day or visit friends? Why not organize your own family car free day – and get your friends to join in too?

1 bus

10 cars

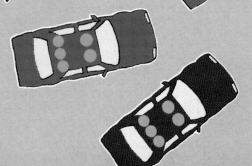

Bus facts

● One bus holds the same number of people as ten full cars.

● A bus takes up four times less road space than ten cars would.

Fumes and the rain

Did you know that exhaust fumes can make a difference to the rain?

Rain gives us all fresh water, but in some places the rain is dirty, or polluted, and harms the plants it falls on. The rain becomes polluted because we burn fossil fuels. The petrol and diesel we put in a car to drive the engine are fossil fuels.

Burning these fuels makes gases, which are acid. The gases are blown into the sky and mix with the clouds. They change the rain that falls from the clouds and make it more acid.

When acid rain falls on trees, it stops the trees growing properly. Their leaves fall off and the trees die. Acid gases can travel a long way on winds which blow around the world.

If the rain falling on these leaves is too acid, it will harm the tree.

What is acid?

Lemon juice, cola and vinegar are all acids. Rain is naturally a bit acid, but the fumes from burning fuels can make it as acid as lemon juice.

I can make a difference

Acid rain is not just caused by fumes from cars. Houses, power stations and factories all burn fossil fuels to make energy, heat and light. Air travel is another big cause of fumes and air pollution. More and more people travel by air every year. If you have a say in where you go on holiday, see if you can help your parents find a way of travelling without flying.

Can we make fuel from plants?

There are some fuels we can burn in engines that don't give off harmful fumes.

In Brazil some people burn fuel made from sugar cane in their car engines instead of petrol or diesel. Cars can't drive as far on this as they can on petrol or diesel, so drivers have to fill their fuel tanks more often. But engines that burn sugar cane fuel puff out less harmful gas.

A driver in Brazil fills his car with fuel made from sugar cane.

One small fact
A car has been made which can run on petrol or sugar cane fuel or both of them mixed together.

Fuel made from plants is called biodiesel. Lots of different things can be made into biodiesel. It can be made from the oil from soya beans, vegetable oils, fat from animals and even used cooking grease.

Sugar cane is loaded on to a truck to go to a biodiesel plant.

When biodiesel is burned in a car engine it doesn't pollute the air as much as petrol or diesel does. But if lots of farmers grow crops for biodiesel instead of food crops, this might mean that people in some countries will not have enough food to eat.

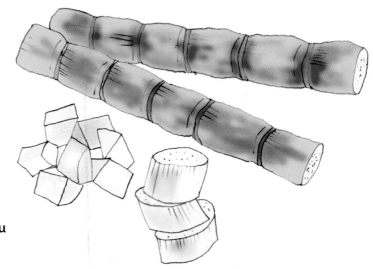

Sugar cane is a grass with thick stems. The sugar is inside the stems, which you can buy to chew.

21

A different sort of car

Scientists everywhere are trying to make energy we can use to get around but which doesn't cause pollution.

One type of car that doesn't puff out polluting gases is the electric car. These are usually small cars which run on an electric battery. This can be recharged when it runs out of energy.

This small Japanese car runs on electricity. It can travel 115 kilometres when the battery is fully charged.

Making less rubbish

Many of the things we use, including cars, often end up being thrown away at a rubbish dump. This means they are not sustainable. Sustainable things need to be made up of materials we can reuse so they don't end up at the dump.

Another idea is that everything we use should be sustainable. That means that the things we use should not cause pollution or harm the natural world around us in any way.

Some engineers have designed a car called the Model U which is sustainable. Its engine burns hydrogen instead of petrol so the car doesn't puff out any polluting gases from its exhaust.

The car's roof is made from corn, which can be turned into compost, and the seats are made from soya beans! This sort of car is a new idea, but maybe one day we'll all be able to drive cars which don't damage the planet.

One small fact
Two million cars are sent to the scrap heap every year in the UK.

Fuel for the future?

We could use a chemical called hydrogen to make our cars go in the future.

Scientists can make hydrogen fuel from water and one day we could use it instead of the petrol we burn in our car engines and the fossil fuels we burn in power stations.

Hydrogen can be put into fuel cells. These fuel cells would give us electricity to run anything from computers and mobile phones to cars and buses. And hydrogen doesn't make polluting fumes. The only thing fuel cells make is water.

Cables take the electricity to a machine that turns water into hydrogen and oxygen.

You need electricity to make hydrogen from water. The electricity could be made by hydropower, using the energy from falling water.

One problem is where to store all the hydrogen. It can be stored as a liquid or a gas and it can explode very easily, so it is a dangerous fuel. Scientists are trying to find a way to store it safely.

The hydrogen is stored in fuel cells and taken to where electricity is needed.

A country run on hydrogen

Iceland wants to be the first country in the world to stop using fossil fuels. Some buses in Iceland, like the one below, already use hydrogen as fuel. By 2050 the plan is for everything in Iceland, even cars, to run on electricity made from hydrogen.

Using the sun's energy

There's another way to travel without polluting the air.

Some teenagers in Australia have built a tricycle that runs on sunshine. The trike has a solar panel. This catches the rays of the sun and turns them into electricity. The electricity charges the batteries which make the trike go.

The Australians took part in a race called the World Solar Cycle Challenge. Every two years people race bicycles powered by the sun over 1500 km of rough ground. Australia and other countries also hold solar races for cars. The challenge is to design a car that can drive a long way using only sunlight as fuel.

There are also races for boats powered by energy from the sun.

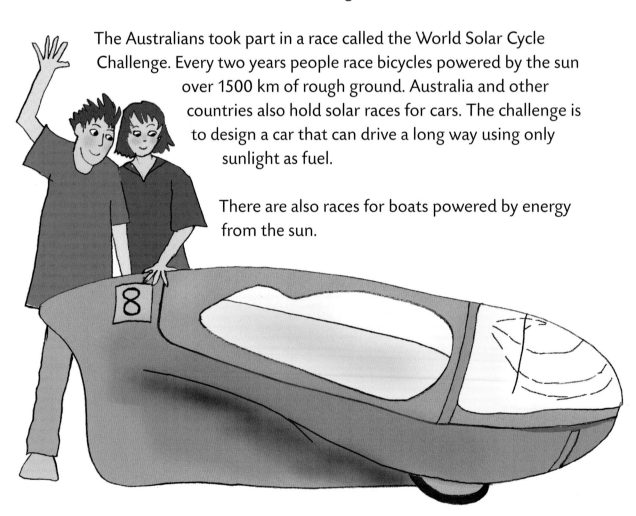

This solar-powered car from Canada took part in the 3000 kilometre Australian World Solar Challenge in 2005.

Why Australia?

Why do you think solar challenge races are held in Australia? (Clue: think about what the weather is like in Australia).

Using less energy

Every journey we make needs energy and the faster and further we want to go, the more energy we need. People in every country in the world need to cut the amount of gases they put into the atmosphere by burning fuel in cars and power stations.

One small fact
If we covered just one per cent of the Sahara Desert with solar panels, we could make enough electricity for the whole world.

Plant trees!

Did you know that trees help to protect the Earth?

Trees take in the gas that our cars and power stations puff out. They take in carbon dioxide and turn it into oxygen which we can breathe. So as well as burning less fuel in our cars and power stations, we need to look after all the trees on Earth, and plant lots more of them.

These children in Kenya are planting trees to help look after the environment.

A campaign called Plant for the Planet is replacing some of the trees that are cut down. The campaign started in Kenya, in Africa, in 2003. Fifty people from 45 countries helped children to plant 4000 trees. Since then, children in Kenya have adopted land where they plant and care for their own trees.

The Plant for the Planet campaign wants lots of other countries to join so that one million trees will be planted by 2013.

But even if people do plant a million trees, it won't make enough difference to the atmosphere. We all need to think about what else we can do, such as driving less, and walking or cycling more, or taking the bus and the train whenever we can.

This young oak tree may live for 200 years. Its leaves take in carbon dioxide from the air and give off oxygen.

I can make a difference

Have a look at the website for Plant for the Planet (see page 31). Could you get together with some friends and organize a school group which can take part? A group of you could make a pledge to plant some trees at school.

Glossary

acid rain
Rain which is dirty or polluted by the fumes from burning fossil fuels.

atmosphere
The thick layer of gases which surrounds the Earth.

carbon dioxide
A gas produced when we burn fossil fuels such as coal or oil. Too much carbon dioxide in the atmosphere leads to climate change.

climate change
Changes in the world's weather which cause more storms and floods.

diesel
A fuel burned in the engines of trucks, buses, trains and some cars.

exhaust fumes
The gases made by burning fuel in an engine.

fossil fuels
Coal, oil and gas are all fossil fuels. They were made over millions of years from living things and we find them under the ground or the sea.

hydrogen
A gas which is very light and which can be made from water.

petrol
A fuel burned in vehicle engines.

pollute
Polluted air, water or land is dirty or dangerous to use or live in.

solar
Relating to the sun.

sustainable
If something is sustainable it can be continued for a long time. Things made from sustainable materials don't harm or pollute the Earth in any way.

Websites

http://www.iwalktoschool.org/
This is the website of International Walk to School, where you can find out about children walking to school in countries all over the world.

http://www.walktoschool.org.uk
Find out about walking to school in the UK on this website.

http://www.walkingbus.com
Loads of info about walking buses.

http://www.bikeability.org.uk
This website tells you about cycle training near you.

http://www.sustrans.org.uk/
Another group which aims to help people cycle more.

http://www.sciencemuseum.org.uk/on-line/energy/
The Science Museum energy website has masses of facts, plus quizzes and case studies from countries around the world.

http://www.unep.org/billiontreecampaign
This website tells you how to help with the Plant for the Planet campaign.

Index

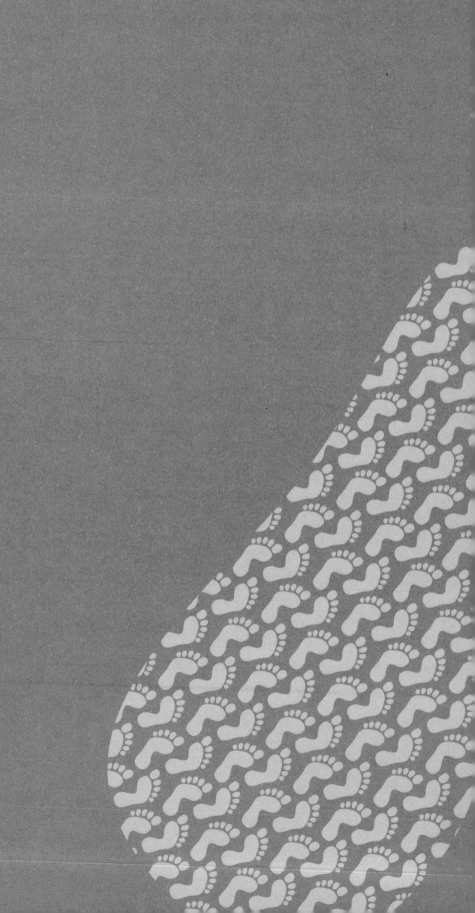